M000196926

The Ultimate

SPORTS TRIVIA

BOOK

The Ultimate

SPORTS TRIVIA

BOOK

The Official Bar Book of Runyon's Saloon

by Tim Hays and Jim Benagh
Illustrated by Paul Rigby

A Citadel Press Book
Published by Carol Publishing Group

Copyright © 1993 by Tim Hays and Jim Benagh
All rights reserved. No part of this book may be reproduced in any
form, except by a newspaper or magazine reviewer who wishes
to quote brief passages in connection with a review.

A Citadel Press Book
Published by Carol Publishing Group

Citadel Press is a registered trademark of Carol
Communications, Inc.

Editorial Offices: 600 Madison Avenue, New York, N.Y. 10022
Sales & Distribution Offices: 120 Enterprise Avenue, Secaucus,
   N.J. 07094
In Canada: Canadian Manda Group, P.O. Box 920, Station U,
   Toronto, Ontario M8Z 5P9

Queries regarding rights and permissions should be addressed to
Carol Publishing Group, 600 Madison Avenue, New York, N.Y. 10022

Carol Publishing Group books are available at special discounts
for bulk purchases, for sales promotions, fund-raising, or
educational purposes. Special editions can be created to specifications.
For details, contact: Special Sales Department, Carol Publishing
Group, 120 Enterprise Avenue, Secaucus, N.J. 07094

Manufactured in the United States of America
10 9 8 7 6 5 4 3 2 1

Library of Congress Cataloging-in-Publication Data
Hays, Tim
   The ultimate sports trivia book : the official bar book of
   Runyon's Saloon / by Tim Hays and Jim Benagh : illustrations
   by Paul Rigby.
         p.   cm.
         ISBN 0-8065-1273-3
         1. Sports-Miscellanea   I. Benagh, Jim   II. Title.
GV707.B44   1993   93-440
796-dc20   CIP

For Anna and Flo and Marlene
and
Dedicated to the memories of
John "Shirts" Hughes, John Carter,
Jay Sharbutt and Art Seidenbaum—
great guys who would've liked this,
and, of course,
to the memory of
Damon Runyon

RUNYON'S and the American Dream

Opened in 1977 by two veteran Manhattan saloonists, Jim Costello and Joe Healey, Runyon's has become the more-or-less home away from home for athletes, coaches, sportswriters, and fun-loving sports fans visiting or living in New York City. The bar is cozy and warm in the cold depths of winter, breezy and cool on a sweltering summer day. Those folks with a vivid interest in sports can find refuge at Runyon's, where the late Pete Axthelm would routinely hold court with fellow sportswriters (and sporting prognosticators), while others such as Mike Lupica of the *New York Daily News* or Mike Francesca of CBS Sports or any of the real breed of sportswriter at the late *National* might meet to review the NBA playoffs or a Ranger game. Visitors such as Digger Phelps, umpire John McSherry, and coach-broadcaster-author John Madden entertain the crowd simply by being there, though generally they're in for a chat with friends or a meal and not to increase their visibility. Neither Costello nor Healey intended Runyon's to become an "in" place, but rather a place to get away from it all.

RUNYON'S AND THE AMERICAN DREAM

Runyon's can probably claim the highest ratio of TV sets to square feet in New York, and on a given day virtually every important sporting event can be seen live, and simultaneously. However, a *caveat* for the *newcomer*—don't ask the mixologist to switch the set from a genuine event, such as a Knick or Ranger game, or a Giant or Jet game, or a Yankee or Met game anytime, to something esoteric such as an interview with some sports figure or a league draft or anything else that's not timely or, most important, *wagerable*. During the 1984 Winter Olympics, a well-dressed gentleman entered Runyon's one Friday evening hoping to have a glimpse of the opening ceremonies. The man approached legendary mixologist John "Shirts" Hughes, who was busy administering to a crowd of regular patrons who were enthusiastically watching the Knicks on one TV, the Rangers on another, and several college basketball games on the other sets. "Do you suppose we could turn one of the TVs over to the opening ceremonies?" the pleasant fellow asked Shirts. "Not unless you can find a way to bet on a parade," Shirts replied, as ever with a warm smile and a wink.

To those who know Runyon's, or who would enjoy hanging out there, enjoy this tribute to insane sports trivia questions.

The road of excess leads to the palace of wisdom.
                              —William Blake

Tim, I think we're on the *autobahn* of excess.
                    —noted golfer James Max Lane IV

That place is so crowded, nobody goes there anymore.
                    —Mr. Berra, our favorite philosopher

Contents

Acknowledgments

No book, however great or small, would be complete without expressions of gratitude to those who helped the authors along and enabled them to finish the work. We will begin with our publisher, Steven Schragis, who agreed with us that while this isn't necessarily Tolstoy or even Stephen King, we nevertheless had a pretty good idea. Steve's belief in this project as we stumbled toward delivery date was validation enough for us. Also, Steve's wife, Donna, who is the world's greatest fan of "The Incredible Hulk," was also supportive of our efforts, though she tastefully disdains both the tobacco smoke and occasional excesses of alcohol that are sometimes witnessed at Runyon's. To Steve and Donna, thanks.

Bruce Bender, President of the Carol Publishing Group, was a tremendous ally. Carole Stuart and her associates Fern Edison and Jessica Black were wonderful in their help in getting the ball rolling and in organizing two pre-publication parties we sponsored at Runyon's during 1990. A nice, long round of applause for the aforementioned, as well as for David Goodnough, Carol's Production Editor.

Now, on to the usual suspects. Jim Costello, who owns

and runs the original Runyon's on Fiftieth Street off Second Avenue (not to be confused with its sister store around the corner on Second Avenue, where on a given night you're more likely to find guys named "Biff" in LaCoste shirts than a good sports argument), gave his blessing to this project from the outset. Of course, you don't have to be Hill and Knowlton or Howard Rubenstein to understand the publicity value of the finished book, either, but Jim graciously consented to let us spread the name and reputation of his fine establishment. (Note to Jim: We better drink free from now on.) The nighttime manager of Runyon's, Jim Frey, who is usually the most sober influence, was also terrific in his hospitality. Frey is also an excellent little-league baseball manager. Jim was patient as we gathered questions from among the regular and irregular patrons, most of whom, like the bartenders, didn't want their real names used (Sorry, dear—Metro North was down again!). One visit to Runyon's and you will understand the desire for anonymity, particularly after a couple of rounds.

The New York *Post*'s Night Sports Editor, Pat Hanigan, known to millions simply as "Hondo," was a great help to the authors in challenging their assumptions and vetting the questions.

To those of our professional colleagues who either helped us out with challenging questions or would admit to knowing us without a fee—ad agency maven Mike Sloser, young and talented sportswriter Vincent Mallozzi, veteran AP war correspondent Richard Pyle, TV producer Judith Bishop, *USA Today Baseball Weekly* National League writer Rob Rains, Barry Bloom of the *San Diego Union Tribune*,

ACKNOWLEDGMENTS

sports-editor-TV-producer-original-New-Orleans-Saint Jerry Lisker, baseball writer Dan Schlossberg, AMEX executive Jennifer Scofield, accountant William Kearns, historian and Ebbets Field expert Roger Newman, Pete Williams of *Baseball Weekly*, and our mothers (could we forget?) deserve special mention.

To those who came up with challenging and, in certain cases, bizarre questions, thank you.

—Tim Hays and Jim Benagh
with Paul Ribgy

Pity the English; a land of sixty different religions—
and only one sauce.

—Voltaire

Too much...is only Chapter One!

—Anonymous

Part One

BASEBALL

Baseball is not just the national pastime here in the United States, it is also the most intellectual, democratic, and logical of all major sports played in this country. Essentially a game in which players of differing skills and varying physical characteristics each contribute to a team's winning effort, baseball entrances most educated Americans from the beginning of Spring Training until the final out of the World Series each year. Proof of baseball's popularity can be found in the two highest-rated World Series of all time. While the television networks sometimes cynically snicker that a World Series will not get good ratings unless a New York or Los Angeles team is in it, the Braves–Twins matchup of 1991, a dramatic contest that lasted seven games (and into the tenth inning at that!) and the Phillies–Royals showdown of 1980 rank as the two highest-rated, most-watched World Series of all time. Just behind them? The 1977 Yankees–Dodgers classic, the Series in which Reggie Jackson came to prominence as "Mr. October" when he smashed three home runs in one game.

Baseball is so universally popular, in fact, that there are some, including the authors, who feel that if the National League had granted franchises to Managua and San Salvador during the 1980s, our relations with both Nicaragua and El Salvador would have been at their all-time best, and war and insurgency would have subsided as people examined their commonalities rather than their differences.

It makes sense, then, that this trivia extravaganza begins with baseball, if you'll pardon our bias toward the sport with more lasting heroes than, say, synchronized swimming, arena football, dwarf-throwing, or ice hockey.

So many significant accomplishments have resulted from performances of individuals who have played baseball that it generally presents the longest-lasting, most challenging questions for sports enthusiasts. An example would be the following. We all remember the 1972 World Series, right? The Oakland A's of the mercurial Charlie Finley versus the Big Red Machine from Cincinnati. Reggie Jackson, Catfish Hunter, and instant-hero Gene Tenace versus Pete Rose, Johnny Bench, Pedro Borbon, and Jack Billingham. That year, the Athletics returned to the Fall Classic for the first time in forty-one years, way back when the franchise was located in Philadelphia. Do you remember the A's' outfield? Good. Now, name the starting outfield that Oakland put on the field in Game One. (*Hint*: Reggie was not among them.) Think about this one for a minute. One of the outfielders was a former batting champion; another was part of a famous "brother" act. When you think you have it, go to the end of this chapter for the correct answer.

The 1991 World Series between the Twins and Braves produced some great moments. Also, because it featured the only teams to rise from the cellar of their respective divisions the year before and meet in the World Series the next year—"From Worst to First," as the wags decreed—it produced some challenging questions as well.

Pitching proved to be the key in the '91 Series. Atlanta, anchored by the Cy Young-winning Tom Glavine and second-year powerhouse Steve Avery, compiled a 2.89 ERA against the Twins, whose 3.74 ERA was made possible courtesy of Jack Morris, the Minnesota native who returned just in time (for the 1991 season). Morris went 2–0 against Atlanta, and his ten-inning, complete-game, Series-clinching shutout in Game Seven was sufficient to get him named MVP. But do you know who the last pitcher was to throw a ten-inning complete game in the World Series? *Hint*: It was twenty-two years between Morris's and this pitcher's CG.

The American public seems to care more about baseball records than about other sports records. For example, Roger Maris and Hank Aaron each received numerous death threats from obsessive fans when they were approaching Babe Ruth's major records—Maris in 1961 when he was closing in on sixty homers in a season, which Ruth had accomplished in 1927, and Aaron during the 1973 and 1974 seasons, when he was fast approaching Ruth's all-time home run record of 714. Tons of angry—and in Aaron's case, racist—mail came across the transoms at Yankee and Braves offices. Distraught fans were beside themselves thinking that a cherished legend was about to be surpassed. In comparison, as great a player

27

as he was, Kareem Abdul-Jabaar wasn't besieged by angry fans as he approached, then broke, Wilt Chamberlain's NBA scoring record.

So... here it is, the first salvo—baseball, the grand and all-consuming national pastime of the U.S. of A. A game even the Russians want to claim as being their invention! Hope you enjoy these questions, culled from experts.

That pitcher who threw the ten-inning win just twenty-two years before Morris? It was Tom Seaver, who beat the Orioles 2–1 in Game Four of the 1969 World Series.

Nes Omnes es potiens victories.
—Official motto of the Red Sox, Indians,
    Angels, Rams, Cubs, Nets,
    Braves, Broncos and Bills

(For those who have neglected their Latin lately,
loosely translated that means, "We can't all
be winners.")

Baseball Questions

Section One

Because this book originated in New York, it is naturally parochial of us to begin with a New York question.

1. Numerous players have spent time with both the Mets and the Yankees. Once, though, it was uncommon, and if a player moved from the Yankees to the upstart Mets, it was deemed to be the end of a career—this in spite of the Mets' first manager, Casey Stengel, having made his name with the Bombers first. Can you name the first player to have gone directly from the Yankees to the Mets?

2. Another New York question. When Babe Ruth had his dynamic, sixty-home-run season in 1927, what number did he wear?

3. What player did Ruth replace in the outfield?

4. Two pitchers allowed Ruth a home run in 1927, and later were victimized by Joe DiMaggio during his fifty-six-game hitting streak in 1941. Who were they?

5. Who were the oldest—and youngest—players to hit fifty home runs in a season?

6. As of 1991, in the World Series, nine players have been ejected from a game. Only one was removed for his own safety, to be protected from unruly fans. Who was he?

7. When Pete Rose got his record-tying 4,191st hit, in what ballpark did he hit it, and who won the game that day?

8. What team, of those that have played in a World Series since 1945, has gone the longest, as of the 1992 Series, without *losing* a Series?

9. Brother acts have been a popular occurrence in baseball. Which brothers hit the most home runs between them?

10. Which brother act has the most pitching victories between them?

11. Which major league batting champion has a brother who won the NFL rushing title two years after brother number one won the batting title?

12. Which pitcher, in the last fifty years, once won twenty-seven games in a season—and was only *second* on his team in victories?

13. There are exactly nine players who have been named MVP in baseball in consecutive years—*one at each*

position. Try naming them. If you really know your baseball, you'll get the pitcher.

14. While we're on the subject of awards, since the inception of the Cy Young Award in 1956, four pitchers have won twenty-five games or more in a season—*and not won the Cy Young.* One of these pitchers is the exemplar of futility—he won twenty-five-plus games *three times* and failed to get the award. Who were the four pitchers—and who was Mr. Frustration?

15. Which pitcher threw two no-hitters, a one-hitter, a two-hitter, and a six-hitter—in the season in which he won only *five games* all year?

16. Which pitcher appeared in a record sixteen World Series games in a three-year period?

17. Whose pitching stopped Joe DiMaggio's fifty-six-game hitting streak?

18. Which team changed its name during the Korean War—for political reasons?

19. Who were the original five players inducted into the Baseball Hall of Fame?

20. Which team had a record *nine* Hall of Famers on it—number nine having been elected and inducted in 1991?

Section Two

1. Bill Veeck was an original thinker as well as a great promoter. What was the title of his seminal memoir?
   a. *An Angel With a Dirty Face*
   b. *My Life in Baseball*
   c. *Veeck, as in Wreck*
   d. *One Leg Up on the Competition*

2. What was the hidden reference and meaning in Veeck's book's title?

3. Eleven players have hit fifty or more home runs in a season. Can you name them?

4. Which famous home run hitter had the most home run seasons matching his uniform number (only numbers over thirty)? *Hint:* When his career was over, his original general manager would say, "I wish I'd given him number 60."

5. Which catcher caught the most no-hitters during his career?

6. Who is the only player ever to win the Triple Crown—and not be named Most Valuable Player?

BASEBALL

7. Who is the only player to hit a home run in the All-Star Game for both leagues?

8. Which team's pitching staffs have never thrown a no-hitter?
   a. Los Angeles Dodgers
   b. New York Mets
   c. Houston Astros
   d. California Angels
   e. San Diego Padres

9. Who are the only players to be named MVP and never play in a World Series?

10. Who among that number was MVP *twice* and didn't make it to the Series?

11. Back to Bill Veeck—which American League team did he buy in the late 1970s?

12. Veeck is probably best remembered for having inserted a very short person into the St. Louis Browns' lineup in an effort to change the strike zone. What was that player's name, what number did he wear, and what was the result of his only plate appearance?

13. Which position player was named MVP despite his not hitting .300, or hitting thirty-plus home runs, or knocking in one hundred RBIs?
   a. Johnny Bench   d. Wilver Stargell
   b. Pete Rose   e. Keith Hernandez
   c. Kirk Gibson

14. Power and speed are a terrific combination in a baseball player. The thirty-thirty plateau, for thirty homers and thirty stolen bases, is a rare achievement. Even rarer is the player who, over his career, shows consistent power and speed. Of the following players, through the 1991 season, which has *not* collected three hundred-plus homers and three hundred-plus stolen bases in his career?
    a. Willie Mays
    b. Fred Lynn
    c. Andre Dawson
    d. Bobby Bonds

15. This will hopefully test your memory well. Which pitcher surrendered both Pete Rose's only grand slam and Jimmy Piersall's one hundredth home run? *Hint:* He later managed a World Series winner.

16. Which pitcher surrendered Hank Aaron's record-breaking 715th home run?

17. Pitchers can be remembered for good days—and bad. Occasionally, they will have a great day. Rick Wise can always remember one outing he had. He pitched a no-hitter, and also did something else that made his team happy. What did Wise do?

18. Who was the last American League switch-hitter to win the MVP Award?

19. Only three times has a pitcher won the Cy Young Award in consecutive years. Which of the following *did not* win the Cy Young two years in a row?

QUESTIONS

a. Roger Clemens
b. Jim Palmer
c. Tom Seaver
d. Sandy Koufax
e. Bob Gibson

20. On to geography: One franchise played in two different cities, yet it never moved. Can you name this mysterious team?

Section Three

1. In what year was the first World Series played, what were the teams, and who won?

2. What is the oldest professional baseball team?

3. Who was the first American League champion to win the World Series?

4. As of this writing, the fall of 1991, which team has gone the longest without winning a World Series?
   a. Boston Red Sox
   b. Chicago Cubs
   c. Cleveland Indians
   d. San Francisco/New York Giants
   e. Atlanta/Milwaukee Braves

5. What was the last World Series to be played by two teams in the same city?

6. What was the last World Series to be played by two teams in the same state?

7. Now, here's a challenge. What was the only World Series to be played by two teams in the same state, the same city, and—*in the same ballpark?*

8. The Oakland Athletics established a dynasty in the 1970s when they put together a team that won three straight World Series. What was the starting outfield in Game One of the 1972 World Series for the A's?

9. After the designated hitter rule was introduced into the American League in 1973, in which World Series was the DH first used, who was the first DH, and how did he perform?

10. What distinction does Danny Cox share with Joaquin Andujar?

11. During the 1981 World Series, when the Yankees traveled to Los Angeles for Games Three and Four, in what hotel did George Steinbrenner have his celebrated argument with an upset fan?

12. By the estimate of the *Los Angeles Times*, how many persons claimed to have witnessed the fight?

13. While the Boston Red Sox have often been frustrated in the World Series—losing most of the times they've appeared—they're nothing next to the California Angels in the futility department. How many times have the Angels come within one game of going to the World Series, only to come from ahead and lose the league championship playoff?

14. Who was the first major league manager to win pennants in both leagues?

BASEBALL

15. Which Braves pitchers became famous not just for their pitching prowess, but for their inclusion in a legendary chant, which ended in "—and pray for rain!"?

16. Which current team has been involved in two World Series, winning both, but losing each road game and winning every home game of both those Series?

17. For which President was Grover Cleveland Alexander named?

18. For whom was Rodney Cline Carew named?

19. For whom was the Baby Ruth candy bar named?

20. One player hit home runs for teams in *all four divisions* of major league baseball one year. Who was he, and what were the teams?

Section Four

Where We Begin to Enter the Bizarre, Exotic, and Strange

1. Since professional baseball started, there has been a total of *nine players* in the majors who have had *five syllables* in their last name. Two of them were brothers, if that helps. Can you name just five of them?

2. Women have played an important role in baseball, even though one has yet to appear in a major league game. One woman was such a great fan that she is the only woman to have been married to a Most Valuable Player in both leagues! Who was she?

3. Who was the first woman to own a major league franchise?

4. What was the last team to finish a season with four twenty-game winners on its pitching staff, and why is it unlikely this will ever again happen?

5. This city broke its record losing streak in 1991 by virtue of its franchise posting the first-ever winning record for a baseball team—and that includes two pro franchises and three minor league teams! What is this formerly futile city? *Hint:* The team fired its manager despite the winning season.

6. Can you name the three players in major league history to play all *nine positions* in one game?

7. Who was the oldest player to get a hit in an All-Star Game?

8. In the center field of Yankee Stadium, where the Hall of Fame plaques are positioned, three ex-Cardinals are enshrined. Can you name them?

9. Though California generally produces the largest number of pro baseball players, both Steve Avery and Jim Abbott hail from this state. Which is it?

10. Jack Morris and Dave Winfield are from this state. Which is it?

11. Who is the only Cy Young Award winner to be born in Mexico?

12. From where does Manny Mota hail?

13. In which country is Dennis Martinez the local hero?

14. What Los Angeles high school produced both Ozzie Smith and Eddie Murray?

15. What Los Angeles high school produced both Darryl Strawberry and former NBA star Marques Johnson?

16. Had Gary Carter not signed with the Montreal Expos organization in 1972, he probably would have listened to the recruiter from a major West Coast school, who wanted him to attend this school—as a football quarterback. What was the school, and with whom would he have competed for the QB slot?

17. What was the meaning of the title of Bob Welch's best-selling book, *Five O'Clock Comes Early*?

18. Can you name five major league catchers who were Jewish? One of them played on the same team on which his brother was a tidy relief pitcher.

19. Which major league franchise has played in the same ballpark the longest time?

20. Since the inception of the NCAA Baseball World Series in 1947, five states have produced *both* an NCAA champion and a World Series winner. Can you name these states, the schools, and the pro teams? (Apologies to Holy Cross and Georgia fans for the pain of the Red Sox and Braves, or there would be seven states.)

21. Through the 1992 World Series, what World Series champion city has been located farthest north?

Our Special Tribute to Joe DiMaggio and Ted Williams

During the 1991 baseball season, American celebrated the fiftieth anniversary of the 1941 rivalry between Joe DiMaggio and Ted Williams, when DiMaggio posted his record fifty-six-game hitting streak while Williams was hitting .406 for the season—two spectacular feats that have yet to be replicated more than fifty years later. Jim Benagh wrote a season-long analysis of the day-by-day play of Williams and DiMaggio, entitled simply "Joe and Ted," that was published each day of the season in the sports section of The New York Times. *Jim became sort of the expert on matters concerning the two legendary players during the 1941 season, and his novel feature was copied by many other newspapers throughout the season.*

Jim and I figured it would be stacking the deck to include his analysis of Joe and Ted in our book, but we each enjoyed the essay that follows, written by our friend Dan Schlossberg, a well-traveled baseball writer. Dan has written three books, and his work appears throughout the United States in many newspapers and magazines. It's with pleasure that we introduce Dan and his essay on Joe and Ted.

—Tim Hays

51

A Tribute to Ted and Joe

Baseball, a game that creates larger-than-life heroes and never forgets them, paused in 1991 to salute the fiftieth anniversary of two of its most celebrated batting feats: Joe DiMaggio's fifty-six-game hitting streak and Ted Williams's .406 season.

In addition to tributes at various ballparks, DiMaggio and Williams were honored at the White House July 9, then flown to Toronto for the All-Star Game aboard Air Force One. White House officials and correspondents hounded them for photographs and autographs en route. Toronto ceremonies honoring the living legends were telecast to an international audience.

President George Bush, who had worshiped Williams as a seventeen-year-old fan of the Boston Red Sox in 1941, summed up the season and the careers of the two Hall of Famers when he said, "DiMaggio bespoke excellence while Williams was John Wayne in a Red Sox uniform."

DiMaggio, right-handed-hitting center fielder of the New York Yankees, was twenty-six and the winner of consecutive batting crowns when the 1941 season started. Williams, twenty-two-year-old left-handed-hitting left fielder

52

of the Boston Red Sox, was starting his third season after hitting .327 and .344 in his first two years. He had led the American League with 145 runs batted in as a rookie in 1939.

On May 15, both men began hitting streaks. Williams hit .487 while connecting in twenty-three straight games, a career high, but DiMaggio continued until July 17, when two backhanded grabs by third baseman Ken Keltner ended the streak in Cleveland.

DiMaggio, who started a new sixteen-game streak the next day, hit .408 during his record skein, while Williams hit .412 over the same span. The Red Sox slugger carried a .405 average into the All-Star break, won the game with a three-run, two-out homer in the ninth, then tacked two points onto his average by September. A late slide dropped the mark to .3996, but Williams went six-for-eight in a season-ending doubleheader to become baseball's first .400 hitter since Bill Terry in 1930. No one has hit higher than .390 since.

"He wouldn't swing at a bad pitch," said fellow Hall of Famer Charlie Gehringer of Williams, who led the American League with 145 walks but struck out only twenty-seven times. "The walks gave him the edge he needed."

Had the current sacrifice fly rule applied in 1941, Williams would have finished at .415. At the time, a sacrifice fly was charged as a time-at-bat without a hit.

Williams led the American League with thirty-seven home runs, while DiMaggio, a .357 hitter, led with 125 runs batted in. DiMaggio won the second of his three Most Valuable Player (MVP) Awards that fall.

Bu the time his career was over, Williams had won two

Triple Crowns, two MVP Awards, and six batting titles while hitting .300 in all but one of his nineteen seasons. He had a .344 lifetime average and 521 home runs.

DiMaggio, who played thirteen seasons, hit .325 with 361 home runs while averaging 118 runs batted in per season. Both men lost considerable time to military service.

"He could do everything," Williams said of DiMaggio. "He had more style than any player I ever knew."

DiMaggio returned the compliment: "Ted Williams was the best pure hitter I ever saw. He was feared."

For the History Books

DiMaggio, who never bunted for a base hit to keep his streak alive, was the ultimate contact hitter in 1941: thirty homers but only thirteen strikeouts.

Even in his third big-league season, Williams was such a scientist in his approach to hitting that he supervised the manufacture of his bats, ordered clubhouse scales to check their weight, and massaged them regularly with olive oil and resin.

Lou Gehrig's death on June 6, three weeks into DiMaggio's streak, depressed the Yankee clubhouse but did not erode the young center fielder's determination.

A spring training ankle injury suffered on March 19 helped Williams by keeping him sidelined for the first two weeks of the season, when the weather was still chilly (a condition Williams abhorred).

A forty-four-game hitting streak by Cincinnati's Pete Rose in 1978 was the closest challenge to DiMaggio's streak, while a .390 average by George Brett in 1980 was the closest challenge to Williams's.

DiMaggio received a Mercedes-Benz during Old Timers Day ceremonies at Yankee Stadium on July 27.

Williams was a real road warrior in 1941, with a .380 average away from Fenway Park and a whopping .485 mark against DiMaggio's Yankees in New York.

DiMaggio had fifteen home runs and fifty-five runs batted in during his streak.

After his ninth-inning double extended the streak to thirty-eight, jubilant teammates gave DiMaggio a bigger demonstration than the 1927 Yankees had given Babe Ruth for his sixtieth homer.

Williams began the season with a thirty-five-inch, thirty-five-ounce bat but was hitting so often to the opposite field that he switched to a thirty-four-ounce bat, enabling him to pull with power toward the right side.

Though debate continues over which feat was greater, most baseball insiders suggest a .400 hitter can have a bad day but compensate later, while a player on a hitting streak must produce every day without fail.

Williams, who enhanced his tough-guy image by distinguishing himself as a fighter pilot in two wars, celebrated his .406 season with a chocolate milkshake.

DiMaggio teammate Tommy Henrich knew the law of averages would eventually end the streak, but said, "He didn't choke. He hit three balls right on the button that night but the odds caught up to him. We knew it would stop sometime."

Williams insists to this day that his game-winning All-Star homer against Claude Passeau was one of the greatest thrills of his career.

Players who have come closest to .406 since 1941: George Brett (.390 in 1980), Rod Carew (.388 in 1977), Ted Williams (.388 in 1957), Stan Musial (.376 in 1949), Tony Gwynn (.370 in 1987).

The longest hitting streak by a player still active was Paul Molitor's thirty-nine-game streak for the 1987 Milwaukee Brewers.

Both DiMaggio and Williams feel their records will fall.

Said DiMaggio: "It would have to be one of those fellows who get 200–220 hits, a guy who can run, bunt, hit to all fields. I was a pull hitter. You've got to make contact and not strike out too much. If you strike out twice in a game, that's taking two shots away from you."

Williams on another .400 season: "It will be done. All it takes is a hitter with some smarts and the dedication to use it. He needs to be a little bit lucky and hit in a hitter's park. It's not going to happen in the Astrodome or Oakland Coliseum. The talent is there if someone would just be disciplined enough. The problem is there don't seem to be any hitters left who want to discipline themselves enough to swing at only good pitches. But somebody will come along who figures that out."

Dan Schlossberg of Fair Lawn, N.J., is Baseball Editor of the *Encyclopedia Americana Annual* and a contributor to many baseball publications.

ANSWERS

Did you sneak to the back of the section first for the 1972 World Series answer? Well, Reggie Jackson was injured, so the starters in Game One of that Series for the A's were...Joe Rudi, Matty Alou, and George Hendrick! Thanks to Jeff Neumann.

Baseball Answers

Section One

1. Marv Throneberry was the first ex-Yankee to play for the Mets when he joined the team in 1962.

2. This is a trick question, natch: Teams didn't have numbers on players' uniforms in 1927.

3. A man who went on to rule the National Football League for years afterwards: George Halas.

4. Ted Lyons of the Red Sox (in both 1927 and 1941) and Lefty Grove, with the Athletics in 1927 and with the Red Sox in 1941.

5. They were the same man—Willie Mays, who hit fifty-one homers in 1955 at age twenty-four and fifty-two in 1965 at age thirty-four.

6. Joe Medwick of the Cardinals was taken out of Game Seven of the 1934 World Series against the Tigers, after

unruly Detroit fans began pelting him with garbage. He hit .379 for the Series, though, and the Cardinals won.

7. The Reds were playing the Cubs at Wrigley, and the game was called for darkness—so there was no result. However, Rose's hit counted. The game was finished at a later date.

8. The Pittsburgh Pirates have a streak of World Series wins dating to 1961, when they beat the Yankees. The last time the Pirates lost a Series, Coolidge was President—in 1927, when Pittsburgh lost to the legendary Yankee team of Ruth.

9. You should have guessed Hank and Tommie Aaron, who combined for 768 homers: Hank, with 755, edged his brother, who hit 13.

10. Phil (318) and Joe (221) Niekro are first with 539 wins, followed by Gaylord (314) and Jim (215) Perry, with 529 between them.

11. Alex Johnson of the California Angels won the AL batting crown in 1970; his brother, Ron, rushed for 1,462 yards with the Giants in 1972 to win the NFL rushing title.

12. Dizzy Trout of the Detroit Tigers won twenty-seven games in 1944, but teammate Hal Newhouser, that year's MVP, won twenty-nine.

13. Fascinating, isn't it, but it's happened exactly once at each position:

ANSWERS

Catcher—Yogi Berra, 1954–55
First Base—Jimmie Foxx, 1932–33
Second Base—Joe Morgan, 1975–76
Third Base—Mike Schmidt, 1980–81
Shortstop—Ernie Banks, 1958–59
Outfield—Mickey Mantle, 1956–57
              Roger Maris, 1960–61
              Dale Murphy, 1982–83
Pitcher—Hal Newhouser, 1944–45

14. Jim Kaat, Ferguson Jenkins, Mickey Lolich, and Juan Marichal, who was three-times frustrated.

15. Virgil "Fire" Trucks of the Tigers was 5–19 in 1952 for a last-place team.

16. Rollie Fingers of Oakland, from 1972–74.

17. Jim Bagby and Al Smith, two very ordinary pitchers for Cleveland, ended DiMaggio's streak on July 17, 1941.

18. The Cincinnati Reds became the Redlegs briefly during the Korean Conflict.

19. In 1936, the first immortals elected to the Hall of Fame were Babe Ruth, Honus Wagner, Christy Mathewson, Ty Cobb, and Walter Johnson.

20. The Yankees of 1934.

Section Two

1. *Veeck, as in Wreck* was the great promoter's book.

2. It was a reference to Veeck's nemesis, former Commissioner Ford Frick. You can figure out the hidden meaning.

3. Maris, Ruth, Mantle, Mays, Foxx, Mize, Kiner, Greenberg, Hack Wilson, Cecil Fielder, and George Foster.

4. Hank Aaron hit forty-four homers while matching his uniform number four times in his career. Former teammate Eddie Matthews made the comment.

5. Jeff Torborg caught four of Nolan Ryan's and Bill Singer's only.

6. In neither of Ted Williams's Triple Crown years—1942 and 1947—was he named MVP.

7. So far, only Frank Robinson has done it.

8. The Mets.

9. Eleven players have been named MVP and not made it to

the World Series, though several still have a shot. Hank Sauer, Ernie Banks, Joe Torre, Dick Allen, Jeff Burroughs, and Rod Carew finished their careers without making it to the Fall Classic. Don Mattingly, Dale Murphy, George Bell, Ryne Sandberg, and Andre Dawson still have a shot.

10. Banks and Murphy.

11. The Chicago White Sox.

12. Eddie Gaedel, the renowned midget, appeared in one at-bat for the Browns, walked on four pitches, and wore number $1/8$.

13. C. Kirk Gibson reached none of those heights when he was named MVP in 1988, though he did lead the Dodgers to a World Series victory.

14. Only Fred Lynn hasn't stolen the three hundred bases to go along with the three hundred homers.

15. Dallas Green.

16. Al Downing of the Dodgers.

17. Wise hit two home runs to go with the no-hitter.

18. A bit tricky—it was Vida Blue, with the A's in 1971.

19. Seaver and Gibson.

20. The Dodgers performed this moving act when the City of Brooklyn merged with the City of New York.

Section Three

1. In 1903 the upstart Boston Red Sox of the two-year-old American League defeated the Pittsburgh Pirates, five games to three.

2. The Cincinnati Reds (Red Stockings)—1871.

3. Those Red Sox—back when they still won World Series.

4. The Indians (1948), Giants (1954), and Braves (1957) are relatively spoiled compared to the Red Sox (1918), but the team that's gone longest without an October victory is the Cubs.

5. The 1956 Series between the Dodgers and Yankees.

6. The 1989 Series between the A's and Giants.

7. The 1944 World Series featured the St. Louis Browns and Cardinals, who both played in Sportsman's Park.

8. Joe Rudi, George Hendrick, and Matty Alou.

9. The 1976 Series between the Reds and Yankees marked the first time a DH was used. Elliott Maddox of the Yankees was first to come to the plate. Sharing DH

responsibilities with Lou Piniella and Carlos May, the DH produced just two hits for the Yankees, while the Reds' Dan Driessen hit .357.

10. Both were ejected from a World Series game.

11. The Wilshire Hyatt.

12. According to the *Times*, there were approximately five hundred witnesses who claimed to be in the elevator with Steinbrenner. The elevator capacity is twelve.

13. In 1986 and 1982 the Angels relinquished leads and missed out on the World Series action.

14. Bobby Cox, with Toronto in 1988 and Atlanta in 1991.

15. (Warren) Spahn and (Johnny) Sain were the two solid pitchers on the Braves staff in 1948.

16. Minnesota won in 1987 and 1991 by winning all its home games while losing every game outside of the Metrodome.

17. Grover Cleveland. We wanted to see if you're up on history.

18. Rodney Cline, the doctor who delivered him.

19. For Grover Cleveland's daughter, Ruth; not for Babe Ruth.

20. Dave Kingman, in 1977, homered for the Mets, Padres, Angels, and Yankees.

Section Four

1. Like this one? Here they are:
   Ed Abbaticchio, Joe Amalfitano, Luis Aparicio, Buddy Biancalana, Pete Castigliore, Pete Incaviglia, Joe Garagiola, and the brothers Conigliaro—Tony and Billy.

2. Mrs. Frank Robinson.

3. Marge Schott of the Reds.

4. Seattle, which had never seen a winning baseball team.

5. Jose Oquendo was the last player to do it; Cesar Tovar and Bert Campaneris preceeded him.
6.
   Carlton Fisk, 43 years old in 1991, at the All-Star Game in Toronto.

7. Baltimore in 1971 (Palmer, Cuellar, McNally, and Dobson), in the days of four-man rotations.

8. Roger Maris, Dizzy Dean, and Cardinal Spellman.

9. Michigan.

10. Minnesota.

11. Fernando Valenzuela.

12. The Dominican Republic.

13. Nicaragua.

14. Manual Arts.

15. Crenshaw.

16. The UCLA Bruins wanted Carter, and he would have been matched with both Mark Harmon and John Sciarra.

17. Cocktail hour begins at five, and it was his near-downfall. The book told of his recovering from alcoholism.

18. Moe Berg, Harry Danning, Ike Danning, Joe Ginsberg, Johnny Kling, and Norm Sherry, whose brother Larry threw for the Dodgers.

19. The Chicago Cubs.

20. California is the easiest, having seen the USC Trojans, Cal State Fullerton Titans, Cal Bears, and Stanford Cardinals win the College World Series while the Dodgers and A's won the big-time show. Also seeing this combination were Michigan, with the U of M and the Tigers; Ohio, with OSU and Cincinnati's Reds; Minnesota, with the Golden Gophers and Twins each winning twice; and Missouri, where the Tigers won at Omaha while the Cardinals and Royals won in October.

21. A. Gotcha! Blue Jay fans. Minnesota, whose Twins hail from Minneapolis, won in 1987 and 1991, on the 45th parallel; Toronto rests south of Minneapolis, near the 43rd.

Part Two

FOOTBALL

Football can easily be called the nation's "second" national pastime, causing men (and women) to become couch potatoes from September through January, when the bowl games and the Super Bowl have been completed. Many famous athletes have come out of football. The Super Bowl is the most-watched TV event of the year, generally, and overseas, other countries have become enthralled with our version of the gladiators. (Japan sends us technology and cheap steel, we send them the Rams and the Lions. Great Britain sends us Andrew Lloyd Webber, we send them the Green Bay Packers and Boston College vs. Army. Interesting balance of cultural payments.)

The following section deals primarily with the NFL, but includes the All-American Football Conference, the World Football League, the United States Football League, college, and assorted other subjects.

Football Questions

1. We'll start off with a simple one. One coach has taken his team to the Super Bowl in three different decades. Who is he?

2. What distinction does Danny Abramowitz hold in the annals of pro football history? *Hint:* Abramowitz broke Lance Rentzel's record for receptions, but that's not the distinction we're looking for.

3. Who is the only NFL coach to win a playoff game with three different teams?

4. In case you overlooked baseball, what NFL rushing champion had a brother who won a major league batting title?

5. What expansion franchise was the quickest to win a Super Bowl?

6. Special teams have become an established and important part of the game. Teams win or lose depending on the success of these special units, once known simply as "suicide squads." Can you name the first team to have

designated "special teams" and the first-ever captain named by his team to head the special teams? *Hint:* His nickname was "Captain Who."

7. What NFL team is nicknamed "the Lambs" due to their sheepish glory in big games?

8. Who am I? One of the most consistent offensive linemen in the NFL for fifteen seasons, I played in four Super Bowls, all with the Vikings. I was the league's number-one draft choice in 1968 after winning the Outland Trophy. I was All-Pro eight times.

9. Who am I? In the longest game in NFL history, I kicked the winning field goal in the second sudden death overtime.

10. Notre Dame has produced the most Heisman Trophy winners. How many of the seven can you name?

11. If you think you know Heisman winners, then you'll easily be able to tell your friends about the only *high school* to produce two Heisman Trophy winners, right? Which school?

12. What Super Bowl hero once insulted Supreme Court Justice Sandra Day O'Connor, telling her to "Loosen up, Sandy baby!"?

13. What play became known as "the mistake by the lake"?

14. Who did Bill Walsh replace as head coach of the San Francisco 49ers?

15. Though I never played in a Super Bowl, having ended my career some years before, I nevertheless led my team to the NFL Championship game four times in the 1950s. We won three of those games, thanks largely to my passing and leadership, and our last championship team scored more points (59) than any titlist since. So, who am I?

16. I once took time out from my job as editor of the *Paris Review* to play quarterback for the same team as the fellow above. It was a brief career, but it provided me with great material for a book. Who am I, pray tell?

17. Who was the legendary defensive back who once insulted Terry Bradshaw before the Super Bowl game between his team and the Steelers, a game Bradshaw won by proving the insulting player wrong?

18. Okay, you've seen Merlin Olsen for almost thirty years, first as a great All-Pro with the Rams, then on television, where he's been ubiquitous. Can you name Olsen's *alma mater*?

19. Art Shell made history when he was named head coach of the Raiders in 1989, becoming the first modern-day Black head coach. But who was the first NFL coach of color, nearly sixty years ago?

20. In his authoritative book *Interference*, author Dan Moldea showed the connection between pro football and what?

21. What was the most common occupation of the majority of the original owners and founders of the NFL?

QUESTIONS

22. The owner of the NFL team for which I coached at the time thought I was a big spender. The owner, a prominent Washington lawyer, once said of me, "I gave—— an unlimited expense account, and he's already exceeded it!" I was also one of the most successful coaches in NFL history. Who am I, and what team was I coaching when the above statement was made? For extra credit, name the owner who made the statement.

23. What college did Buddy Ryan attend? *Hint:* Dallas coach Jimmy Johnson led it to probation while coaching there.

24. At which prominent West Coast university did Al Davis toil as an assistant coach before leaving for the AFL? He led it, too, to probation.

25. All right, old-movie buffs! In the classic film *Number One*, Charlton Heston played a pro quarterback for what team?

26. Speaking of movie legends, what is the importance of Knute Rockne saying to George Gipp's teammates, "Win this one for the Gipper!"?

27. My brother and I are both pretty famous pro football players, though he's been retired for years while I'm one of the NFL's most versatile quarterbacks. My brother once scored four touchdowns in a Rose Bowl game, playing for USC. Can you name my brother and me?

28. What do the following three teams have in common: the Rams, the Browns, the Lions?

29. Which of the following players *did not* win the Heisman Trophy during his carrer at USC?
    a. Mike Garrett
    b. Ricky Bell
    c. Charlie White
    d. Marcus Allen

30. I played for the New York Giants during the 1950s and '60s. I was pretty modest, but my teammates liked me so much that *six* of them named sons after me. Who am I?

31. In New York City, each of the five boroughs has been home at one time or another to an NFL franchise. Can you name every team, matched with its proper home borough?

32. What real-life occurrence formed the basis for John Madden's renowned "fear of flying"?

33. What do the following four teams have in common: the Jets, the Chiefs, the Dolphins, the Raiders?

34. Only two Heisman Trophy winners have later been named Most Valuable Player in the NFL as recipients of the Jim Thorpe Award. One of the two was named MVP three times. Can you name both players?

35. Who succeeded Vince Lombardi as coach of the Green Bay Packers?

36. Who replaced Don Shula as head coach of the Baltimore Colts?

37. How often has a star player from a national college football championship team led his team to the Super Bowl in his first season in the pros?

38. Only two cities known for cold winter weather have hosted a Super Bowl game. Which cities were they, what years, and what were the circumstances surrounding the NFL's decision to play the normally warm-weather game in those cities.

39. The 1983 professional draft is famous for having produced a number of great quarterbacks. Through 1993, what is the singlemost distinction of the Class of '83.

Football Answers

1. Don Shula of the Colts and Dolphins: in 1969 with the Colts, and in 1972, '73, '83, and '85 with the Dolphins.

2. Abramowitz was the last legitimate pick in the 1967 draft (number 437).

3. Chuck Knox, with the Rams (1973–77), Buffalo ('81), and Seattle (1983–88).

4. Ron Johnson of the 1972 Giants and Alex Johnson of the 1971 Angels.

5. The Dolphins were in the league just six years before winning it all.

6. Alex Hawkins, the renowned "Captain Who?" of the Baltimore Colts, in 1966, was the first special teams captain.

7. The LA Rams.

8. Ron Yary of the Vikings and USC.

9. Garo Yepremian of the Miami Dolphins, 1971 vs. Kansas City.

FOOTBALL

10. Angelo Bertelli, Johnny Lujack, Leon Hart, John Lattner, Paul Hornung, John Huarte, Tim Brown.

11. Highland Park High School in Dallas produced both Doak Walker and Tim Brown.

12. It was the irrepressible John Riggins of the Redskins.

13. The pass interception thrown by Brian Sipe in the 1980 AFC playoff game between Cleveland and Oakland. Picked off by Lester Hayes, it ended Cleveland's comeback drive.

14. Monte Clark.

15. Bobby Layne of the Detroit Lions.

16. George Plimpton.

17. Thomas Henderson, then known by the nickname "Hollywood."

18. Utah State.

19. Fritz Pollard of Akron in 1921.

20. Gambling and organized crime.

21. They were mostly legal bookmakers and racetrack owners, though the euphemism at the time was "sportsmen."

22. George Allen was the coach of the Washington Redskins. Edward Bennett Williams made the comment.

23. Oklahoma State.

ANSWERS

24. USC.

25. Heston toiled for the New Orleans Saints.

26. He never actually said it. It was entirely cinema.

27. Randall Cunningham and Sam "The Bam" Cunningham of UNLV and USC.

28. Each was an old-line NFL or AAFC franchise that won an NFL Championship prior to the 1966 merger with the AFL.

29. Ricky Bell was the only one not to win the Heisman.

30. Kyle Rote—imagine six godchildren namesakes!

31. Manhattan—Giants and Titans (Jets); Staten Island—Stapletons; Queens—Jets; Bronx—Giants; Brooklyn—Dodgers.

32. The plane crash of the 1960 Cal Poly football team.

33. Each was an original AFL team that has won the Super Bowl since the 1966 merger.

34. O. J. Simpson (once) and Earl Campbell (three times).

35. Phil Bengtson.

36. Don McCafferty, who won the title in his second year.

37. If you can come up with someone other than Tony Dorsett, you're better than we are.

38. Detroit, in 1982, as the NFL tried to lend a hand to the city's declining economy. Minneapolis was the site of Super Bowl XXVI for its domed stadium alone.

39. A. Though each of the seven has had respectable careers, none has yet won a Super Bowl, though five have been there and lost. Todd Blackledge and Ken O'Brien have yet to start in a Super Bowl; Dan Marino (1985), Tony Eason (1986), and Boomer Esiason (1989) have been there once and lost; Jim Kelly (1991–93) joined John Elway (1987–88, 1990) as thrice unlucky in Super Bowl XXVII.

Part Three

THE NBA

The NBA

The National Basketball Association has been around since 1946. Arguably the most physically demanding of the major league sports, with hockey a close second, basketball has produced a number of great sports legends—and records—as a result of which hoop fans enjoy quizzing one another. Because of the evolution of play since 1946, from a slow style relying mainly on outside shooting to the significant dependence on the interior big men to the fast-break teams of the 1980s and 1990s where a six-foot-nine guard was no longer quite an oddity, differing styles of play have resulted in changing importance in statistics. Where, for example, rebounding was once the most telling stat (when Wilt and Russell would dominate the middle and grab twenty-five per game), the maturity of shooting has lessened the importance of great numbers of rebounds. In the 1960s and '70s, guards and forwards who converted 50 percent of their shots were rare; in the 1980s and now '90s, anyone not accurate half the time is likely to find himself in the CBA—or worse.

Keep the above in mind when trying to answer the question in the next section.

The Players

Who is the greatest basketball player who ever lived? Bill Russell? Wilt Chamberlain? Bill Walton? Kareem Adbul-Jabaar? Magic Johnson? Or perhaps Michael Jordan? Larry Bird? Each basketball fan has his or her own opinion. Perhaps Bob Pettit, a six-nine forward, is still the best example of a pro hoops player—yet, half the people living today never saw Pettit play, although he retired only twenty-five years ago, in 1965. After graduating from LSU in 1954, Pettit played eleven years with the Milwaukee, then St. Louis, Hawks (a team now at home in Atlanta) and was chosen for the NBA All-Star team *eleven* times—this, when the All-Stars were chosen by the coaches and writers, not by the fickle fans. Pettit averaged twenty-six points and sixteen rebounds a game in those eleven years, a period in which the Hawks went to the NBA playoffs nine times. He was MVP twice, in 1956 and 1959, before Russell and Chamberlain revolutionized the game. He was NBA Rookie of the Year (1955), and MVP of the All-Star Game in 1956, '58, '59, and '62. Yet he wears only one NBA Championship ring—from 1958, when the Hawks beat the Celtics. If he were playing today, Bob Pettit might make twelve million dollars or so annually, comparing him to today's high-tech stars.

Questions—NBA

1. The easiest question first: Who is the only NBA player to lead the league in scoring, rebounding, *and* assists at some point in his career?

2. Only four players have averaged twenty points *and* twenty rebounds per game during the same season. Who were they?

3. Only one player has been named MVP of the NBA *and* MVP of the All-Star Game *and* Playoff MVP *in the same season.* Who was he? What year?

4. In the NBA draft, three players from the *same high school* were selected one year in the first round. All three were college players. Who were they, and what was their high school?

5. What NBA player averaged thirty points *and* ten assists—five times in his career? *Hint:* He's the only one to do it *once.*

6. Gathering ten thousand-plus rebounds while scoring ten thousand-plus points in the course of a career is quite an accomplishment, so much so that only eighteen players

have done it in the NBA's first forty-four years. Which of the following *did not* accumulate twin ten thousands?

a. Bill Bridges
b. Larry Bird
c. Moses Malone
d. Johnny Kerr
e. Paul Silas

7. Only one player who wasn't a center was named MVP of the NBA during the period of the big man, from 1960 to 1980. Who was he?

8. Only two players have ever been named MVP *and* Rookie of the Year in the same year. Who were they?

9. Only one player grabbed more than ten thousand rebounds in his career without averaging at least ten per game. He is also the only player to manage ten thousand-plus rebounds without scoring ten thousand points. Who was he?

10. Scoring points can be glamorous, but how many times since 1960 has the NBA scoring champion led his team to the NBA Championship?

11. Who of the following was never named NBA MVP?
a. Julius Erving
b. Oscar Robertson
c. Dave Cowens
d. Jerry West

12. Who was the last NBA center to average fifteen rebounds per game over a season? *Hint:* He played at UCLA.

QUESTIONS

13. Now a literary question: What team was immortalized in author David Halberstam's *The Breaks of the Game*?

14. And a cinematic question: What team did Julius Erving play for in the all-time classic. *The Fish That Saved Pittsburgh*?

15. Only four teams that were charter members of the NBA in 1946 are still playing. Who are they?

16. Which of the following NBA players *did not* average twenty points and twenty rebounds per game during his NCAA career?
    a. Bill Russell
    b. Paul Silas
    c. Artis Gilmore
    d. Bill Walton
    e. Jerry Lucas

17. Who is the only person in the Basketball Hall of Fame as *both* a coach *and* a player?

18. Only one player has collected more than one thousand assists in a season more than once. Who is he, what college did he attend, and who has been his favorite teammate to dish those assists to?

19. What back-up center to Bill Russell later coached an NCAA champion?

20. Who is the only player to lead his high school, college, and pro teams to the championship—all in four years?

NBA FINALS

The NBA Finals are the most grueling trial in sports. After eighty-two regular season games, teams have got to play three series just to get to the championship round, then hope to endure long enough to win the title. Not quite the Bataan Death March, but physically demanding. Therefore, accomplishments in the championships are usually more significant than those of the regular season.

Questions—NBA Finals

1. What is the significance of the Boston Celtics losing in the 1991 NBA playoffs?

2. Which of the following teams has never won an NBA Championship?
   a. Atlanta Hawks
   b. Houston Rockets
   c. Sacramento Kings
   d. Golden State Warriors

3. Which of the following has played in the most NBA Championship finals?
   a. Los Angeles Lakers
   b. Boston Celtics
   c. New York Knicks
   d. Detroit Pistons

4. Who won the first NBA Championship series?
   a. Boston Celtics
   b. Los Angeles Lakers
   c. Golden State Warriors
   d. New York Knicks

5. Which coach has coached an NBA champion with more than one team?
   a. Bill Sharman
   b. Jack Ramsay
   c. Alex Hannum
   d. Bill Fitch

6. Who was the starting center for the Los Angeles Lakers in Game Six of the 1980 NBA Finals, when the Lakers beat Philadelphia to clinch the NBA title?

7. Who was the only player from the *losing* team to be named MVP in the finals? What was the year, who were the teams?

8. Who are the only three coaches of NBA Championship teams who played on an NCAA Championship Game?

9. What NBA Final became known by the expression "The fat lady finally sings!"? What coach coined that phrase?

10. Who were the starting centers in that final?

11. When the Milwaukee Bucks won the 1970–71 NBA Championship, what was the significance of their victory?

12. Who was the starting center on the two NBA champions that boasted the two best winning percentages in NBA history?

13. Who are the five coaches to take two different teams to the NBA Finals? *Hint:* The earlier question referred to the only one who *won* with both teams.

14. Who holds the record for most points scored in an NBA Final game (61)?
    a. Kareem Abdul-Jabaar
    b. Elgin Baylor
    c. Wilt Chamberlain
    d. Jerry West

15. Who are the only two NBA regular season scoring champions since 1958 to play on an NBA Championship team the same year?

16. Conversely, three NBA assists leaders have led their team to the NBA Championship the same year. Who were they? *Hint:* Two of them played for the same team at different times.

17. Finally, one university produced the only two coaches in history to win both an NBA Championship *and* an American Basketball Association title. One of the two won NBA titles with two different teams. *Hint number one:* The center on both coaches' last NBA champion was the same player. *Hint number two:* The second coach's team broke a record set by the first coach's team. What was their *alma mater*, who were the coaches, what were the teams, who was the common center, and what record was broken?

Answers—NBA

1. Wilt Chamberlain.

2. Back when rebounding was more prolific, before shooting percentages increased, four players did it—and none since the late 1960s. The four are Bob Pettit, Wilt (of course), Jerry Lucas, and Nate Thurmond.

3. Willis Reed in 1970.

4. Baltimore's Dunbar High School produced Reggie Williams, Muggsy Bogues, and Reggie Lewis, who were all drafted in the first round of the 1987 NBA draft.

5. Oscar Robertson.

6. Larry Bird.

7. Oscar Robertson in 1963.

8. Wes Unseld in 1968.

9. Leroy Ellis, a product of St. John's.

10. Three times—this last year, in 1991 and 1992, Michael Jordan led the NBA in scoring and the Bulls won the

title; before that, you have to go back twenty years to 1971, when Kareem Abdul-Jabaar led the league in scoring and took the Bucks to the championship.

11. Jerry West, but it was sort of like Marichal never winning the Cy Young Award. West always finished in the top five or ten in the MVP balloting, but usually Wilt, Russell, Oscar Robertson, or Kareem took the prize.

12. Another trick question—it was Swen Nater, then of San Diego, in 1979.

13. The Portland Trailblazers.

14. The Pittsburgh Pisces.

15. The Knicks, the Warriors, the Celtics, and the Hawks.

16. Bill Walton.

17. John Wooden.

18. John Stockton of the Jazz. He attended powerhouse Gonzaga of Washington, and has made a living of passing to Karl Malone.

19. John Thompson.

20. If you know anyone other than Magic Johnson who's done it, write us. Magic led his high school team to the Michigan State Championship in 1977; then, as a sophomore at MSU, won the NCAA Championship in 1979; then, as a rookie with the Lakers, led LA to its first of five 1980s titles in 1980. Four seasons and three championships, all at different levels.

Answers—NBA finals

1. With their last title coming in 1986, it marked the longest time in the Celtics' history (since 1957) that the team had gone *without winning* an NBA Championship. Previously, Boston had never gone more than five years without a title.

2. The Rockets, of course, though this was deliberately tricky. The Warriors, then in Philadelphia, won the first NBA title, in 1946–47, followed by their 1975 upset of the Washington Bullets. The Kings, playing in Rochester as the Royals, won it all in 1950–51. The Hawks, still in St. Louis, interrupted the Celtics' streak of titles by winning in 1957–58.

3. The Lakers, with twenty-four appearances. The Celtics have been to the finals nineteen times, the Knicks six times, the Pistons only thrice.

4. The Warriors, then playing in Philadelphia.

5. Alex Hannum is still the only one to *win* with two teams: the Hawks in 1957–58 and the 76ers in 1966–67.

6. Magic Johnson replaced Kareem Abdul-Jabaar for that game; Abdul-Jabaar was ill and stayed in LA as the Lakers traveled to Philadelphia where Magic scored forty-two points in the post and the Lakers clinched the title.

7. Jerry West, 1969, in the Lakers' seven-game loss to the Celtics.

8. K. C. Jones and Bill Russell from University of San Francisco and the Celtics, and Pat Riley at Kentucky and the Lakers. Jones and Russell won the NCAAs; Riley's Wildcats were upset by Texas Western (now UTEP).

9. The irrepressible Dick Motta, coach of the 1977–78 Washington Bullets, was fond of saying "It ain't over till the Fat Lady sings," probably due to his frequent visits to hear *Tosca* at the Met; when the Bullets beat the Supersonics that year, the headlines in Washington and Baltimore papers exclaimed, "She sings!"

10. Wes Unseld and Jack Sikma.

11. The Bucks became the expansion team to win the NBA title in the quickest time—three years. Kareem Abdul-Jabaar and Oscar Robertson led Milwaukee to the promised land.

12. Wilt Chamberlain, though he's sometimes forgotten for this accomplishment—with the 76ers in 1967 and with the Lakers in 1972.

13. K. C. Jones, Alex Hannum, Bill Fitch, and, surprise, Red Auerbach, Jones losing in his first trip with the

Bullets in 1975, winning later with the Celtics; Hannum in 1957–58 with those Hawks and in 1966–67 with the 76ers; and Fitch in 1981 with the Celtics and later in 1986 with the Rockets, where he saw Jones and the Celtics deny him the chance to match Hannum. Bill Sharman, in 1966–67 and 1971–72 (Warriors, Lakers). Auerbach lost in the 1949 finals with the Washington Capitals, before collecting a few titles with Boston.

14. Elgin Baylor, in 1962.

15. Kareem Abdul-Jabaar, when he led the Bucks to the title in 1970–71, and Michael Jordan, whose scoring led the Bulls to titles in 1991 and 1992.

16. Bob Cousy, with the Celtics several times; Jerry West, with the Lakers in 1971–72; and Magic Johnson with the Lakers several times.

17. The University of Southern California spawned both Bill Sharman and Alex Hannum. Hannum coached the 1957–58 Hawks, the 1966–67 76ers, and the 1968–69 Oakland Oaks; Sharman coached the 1970–71 Utah Stars and the 1971–72 Lakers. Wilt was the common NBA center. The 76ers had the best regular season winning percentage (68–13, .839) until his old buddy Sharman produced a 69–13 record, or .841, with the Lakers. Sharman also coached a titlist in the short-lived ABL.

Part Four

THE NHL

For you fans of the ice, we're including some real challenging questions about the Canadian national pastime. Though it's been more than fifty years since the Rangers brought home the Stanley Cup, like Cubs and Red Sox fans, you folks who live and die with Madison Square Garden's home team are leading the league in patience! For those lucky enough to live in Boston, Long Island, Pittsburgh, Edmonton, or Montreal, you should feel for your Ranger colleagues.

See how good your hockey knowledge is!

NHL Questions

1. Billy Smith of the Islanders was the first goalie to score a goal. However, a goalie for another team actually scored a goal before Smith, while he was not in goal. Who was it?

2. Who was the starting goalie on that last Ranger team, in 1940, that won the Stanley Cup?

3. Many players have scored fifty goals in a season, the benchmark of an offensive hockey player's season or career. Who reached fifty goals in a season in the quickest time—that is, in the fewest games?

4. Before 1991, when Minnesota and Pittsburgh met in the Stanley Cup Final, when was the last time two *American* teams met there?

5. In the Stanley Cup playoffs, two players have scored *four* goals in one period. Who were they?

6. Who was the first rookie to score five goals in one game?

7. The National Hockey League is not yet known as a haven for Black players, yet several have played, some with

great distinction. Who was the NHL's first Black player, and for whom did he play?

8. When the Boston Bruins traded Phil Esposito and Carol Vadnais to the Rangers for Brad Park and Jean Ratelle, the Rangers threw in another, less famous player along with Park and Ratelle. Who was he?

9. Two players have recorded six assists in a playoff game. Who were they?

10. Sometimes hockey coaches and referees get into heated exchanges with one another that remind the hockey fan of a good baseball argument. Which NHL coach, in a playoff game, told referee Don Koharski, "Have another doughnut, you fat pig!"?

NHL Answers

1. Ron Hextall of Philadelphia scored an empty-net goal against the Boston Bruins on December 9, 1987.

2. Davie Kerr, who won the Venzina Trophy in 1940 as the NHL's best goalie.

3. Who else but Wayne Gretzky, accumulating fifty goals in just thirty-nine games in the 1981–82 season.

4. Before the Pittsburgh Penguins beat the Minnesota North Stars in the 1991 Stanley Cup Finals, it had been way back in 1981 when the New York Islanders beat those same North Stars.

5. Tim Kerr of the Flyers was first to do it, scoring four goals against the Rangers on April 13, 1985. Four years later, Mario Lemieux did it against the Flyers.

6. Howie Meeker of the Maple Leafs scored five goals in one game, in 1947.

7. Remember Willie O'Ree? He played two games for Boston in 1957–58.

8. The throw-in player was Joe Zanussi, who would score only two points as a Bruin.

9. Mikko Leinonen of the Rangers was first to do it on April 8, 1982; Gretzky repeated the feat when he was still with Edmonton, getting six assists against the Kings on April 9, 1987.

10. Jim Schoenfeld of the Devils was guilty of this most infamous exchange between a coach and referee.

Part Five

THE NCAA

The NCAA is the proving ground for future professional athletes. Some schools, of course, take that more seriously than others—Oklahoma State, USC, UNLV, any school in the Southwest Conference—but the devotion of those schools to winning doesn't distract those of us who are fans. The intensity of a SC–Notre Dame November football game is twice as exciting as, say, the Browns and Colts at any point during their season. When Michigan or Florida State or Miami, or even, on occasion, East Carolina, is engaged on the gridiron, the TV fans are tuned closely to the game. If St. John's or Syracuse or North Carolina is playing a mid-season basketball game in the Big East or ACC, that's exciting, whereas the Cavaliers versus the Kings in the NBA may leave an audience yawning.

Now, test your memory of college sports trivia.

NCAA Questions

1. Starting off with college football, there are two states that have each produced *seven* Heisman Trophy winners. Can you name the states, the Heisman winners, and the schools they attended?

2. The first winner of the Heisman Trophy was also the first person ever selected in an NFL draft. Can you name him?

3. Can you name the only two schools to rank in the Top 15 in wins in both football and basketball since the beginning of NCAA competition? *Hint:* Neither UCLA or Oklahoma is one of them.

4. Five schools have won the NCAA Basketball Championship *and* have seen their football team ranked number one in a post-season poll—only five. Four of them are in two states. Who are they?

5. Tiny Weber State College in Provo, Utah, has produced two successful pro basketball coaches. Who are they?

6. "Wildcats" is a popular college nickname. Can you name NCAA champions in basketball and baseball to share that nickname?

7. What school won the first NCAA Basketball Championship? They haven't come close since, having ducked the competition.

8. The Heisman Trophy was named for the coach at which school?

9. Reggie Jackson established himself at the same college where Frank Kush coached football. Which school?

10. Tom Seaver and Fred Lynn attended this West Coast school—and in between their years, a Heisman Trophy-winning player was also All-America in baseball there. Name the school and the Heisman winner.

11. Steve Garvey and Bubba Smith went to what Midwest school.

12. In sportscasting and sportswriting, several schools have produced some distinguished alumni. Which Big East school did Marv Albert and Bob Costas attend?

13. Which school produced, among others, Curry Kirkpatrick of *Sports Illustrated*, David Brinkley (he only likes sports), and Jim Lampley, of NBC Sports?

14. Gerald Ford was an All-America lineman at which Big Ten school?

15. Former President Bush was captain of the baseball team at which school?

16. Only one school other than UCLA won an NCAA Basketball Championship from 1964 to 1972. What was the name of this school when it won the title, and for which sport is it best known?

17. Who was the legendary baseball coach at USC whose legacy includes seven NCAA Championships and numerous All-America (and pro) players—all this, while serving for just one dollar a year?

18. At which Midwest school did the outspoken (and best-selling) Dick Vitale establish himself as a college basketball coach?

19. Don Coryell established himself as football coach at which school?

20. Bobby Knight established himself at what prominent school in his first coaching job.

21. Pete Newell is regarded as one of the best basketball minds ever. Which western school did he coach to an NCAA Championship?

22. The year Newell led the above team to the championship, which eastern school did his team beat, and who was the star of that team? (That star later was a perennial All-Pro NBA player, and is still active as president of an NBA team.)

23. Which former Providence coach was responsible for founding the Big East Conference?

24. Which Big East school is the *alma mater* of LA Raiders owner Al Davis?

NCAA

25. Which school did Pat Riley, Kyle Macy, and Sam Bowie attend, each of them playing in a Final Four?

26. Since the beginning of the NCAA Basketball Tournament in 1939, seven states have produced two or more different schools that have won the Final Four title. One of these seven states has *three* winners and another has *four* different winners. This will test your college basketball knowledge—but don't run to the Almanac. Try getting all seven states and all the schools, bearing in mind two of them are tough—but think about famous explorers.

NCAA Answers

1. California and Ohio. California—Mike Garrett, O. J. Simpson, Charles White, and Marcus Allen (USC); Gary Beban (UCLA); Jim Plunkett (Stanford); Glenn Davis (Army). Ohio—Archie Griffin (counts twice), Vic Janowitz, Hopalong Cassady, and Les Horvath (OSU); Dick Kazmaier (Princeton); Roger Stauback (Navy).

2. Jay Berwanger of the University of Chicago.

3. Syracuse and Notre Dame.

4. Michigan and Michigan State; Ohio State; UCLA and Stanford.

5. Dick Motta and Phil Jackson.

6. Kentucky (basketball), Arizona State ,(baseball), and Villanova (basketball).

7. Oregon (the Ducks).

8. John Heisman of Auburn.

9. Arizona State.

10. USC. Mike Garrett was the two-sports star.

11. Michigan State.

12. Syracuse.

13. The University of North Carolina.

14. Michigan.

15. Yale.

16. Texas Western was its name when it was NCAA champion in 1966. It is now the University of Texas–El Paso. Track is its most prominent sport.

17. Raoul (Rod) Dedeaux. A former All-America himself, Dedeaux had become financially successful with his trucking company.

18. The University of Detroit.

19. San Diego State.

20. Army.

21. California, in 1959.

22. West Virginia, which was led by Jerry West, now president of the Lakers.

23. Dave Gavitt.

24. Syracuse.

25. Kentucky.

26. *California*
Stanford (1942), USF (1955–56), Cal (1959) and UCLA (1964–65, 1967–73, 1975) are the four.

ANSWERS

North Carolina
UNC (1957, 1982), NC State (1974, 1983), and Duke (1991–92) are the three.

Kentucky
UK (1948–49, 1951, 1958, 1978) and Louisville (1980 and 1986) tie the Bluegrass State with Carolina for second most NCAA titles (six).

Ohio
OSU in 1960 and Cincinnati in 1961 and '62 brought home three years of championships. Will Cincy break the state's 33-year drought?

Michigan
The most recent state to boast a title twosome, UM in 1989 added to Magic's 1979 victory.

The toughest in the authors' opinion?
Pennsylvania, with Villanova (1985) joining LaSalle's Explorers of 1954; and *Wisconsin*, whose UW Badgers won the third NCAA tourney in 1941 and were joined in 1977 by Al McGuire's *Marquette* team.

Appendix

Statistical Accuracy

The questions and answers contained in *The Ultimate Sports Trivia Book* are valid as of July 15, 1991, and include the 1990–91 NBA and NCAA Championships, the 1991 Super Bowl, and the 1991 major league baseball season through the All-Star break. Most important, of course, is that Super Bowl XXV, the Desert Storm-interrupted game in which the Giants edged the Bills, 20–19. (Co-author Benagh would have won a substantial sum, approximately eight thousand dollars, in a pool here in Manhattan had the Giants, on their final drive which resulted in a winning field goal, elected instead to go for a touchdown on fourth down. That would have meant a final score of 24–19. Jim had NFC—4, AFC—9 in his pool. So, the conservative approach by Giant coach Bill Parcells, winner of two Super Bowls, cost my pal eight thousand dollars. I, on the other hand, being a conservative bettor, wagered twenty-one dollars on the Giants, straight up.)

APPENDIX

The baseball answers are valid through the 1990 World Series, which was won, valiantly, by the Cincinnati Reds, who were managed by Lou Piniella, the ex-Yankee manager. Remember that Series? The powerhouse Oakland A's, managed by Tony LaRussa, one of only five baseball managers in history to have earned a law degree (the other four are in the Hall of Fame—LaRussa should, to paraphrase Parcells when speaking of Lawrence Taylor, "rollerskate to Cooperstown"), faded fast, losing the series in five short games. There was no war in the Persian Gulf then—only a buildup of troops, none related to any of the A's).

In most cases, the reference sources are: *The Baseball Encyclopedia* (Macmillan, 1992, Rick Wolff, Editor); *The NBA Register* and *NBA Guide* (The Sporting News Publishing Company, 1993); *The New York Times*, *New York Post*, *New York Daily News*, and *The World Almanac* (Pharos Books/UME, 1991). Thanks also to Jeff Neumann for his vetting of certain baseball questions. The authors, however, accept full responsibility for the accuracy of every question contained here, including the bizarre questions, and do not blame any brewery or other beverage company for any mistakes, though they almost took the Twelve Steps while compiling this book.

TH and JB
July 1993

Sports Books Ordering Information

Ask for any of the books listed below at your bookstore. Or to order direct from the publisher, call 1-800-447-BOOK (MasterCard or Visa), or send a check or money order for the books purchased (plus $3.00 shipping and handling for the first book ordered and 50¢ for each additional book) to Carol Publishing Group, 120 Enterprise Avenue, Dept. 1273, Secaucus, NJ 07094.

Settle-Your-Bet Sports Trivia Books
Questions, Answers (and Photos) Covering Every Professional Sport Team--Past & Present--From the Following Cities:

Boston Sports Quiz by Brenda Alesii & Daniel Locche; Paperback $9.95 (#51212)

Chicago Sports Quiz by Brenda Alesii & Daniel Locche; Paperback $9.95 (#51372)

Los Angeles Sports Quiz by Brenda Alesii & Daniel Locche; Paperback $10.95 (#51381)

New York Sports Quiz by Brenda Alesii & Daniel Locche; Paperback $10.95 (#51215)

Philadelphia Sports Quiz by Brenda Alesii & Daniel Locche; Paperback $9.95 (#51416)

The Ultimate Sports Trivia Book: The Official Bar Book of Runyon's Saloon by Jim Benagh & Tim Hays; Paperback $8.95 (#51273)

Washington/Baltimore Sports Quiz by Brenda Alesii & Daniel Locche; Paperback $9.95 (#51424)

Tennis Books

Love Match: Nelson vs. Navratilova by Sandra Faulkner w/Judy Nelson; Hardcover w/16 pages of photos. $19.95 (#72157)

Winning Ugly: Mental Warfare in Tennis by Brad Gilbert & Steve Jamison; Hardcover w/8 pages of photos. $18.95 (#72169)

World Tennis Magazine's Guide to the Best Tennis Resorts by Peter Coan w/Barry Stambler; Paperback $10.95 (#51272)

Sports Jokes

The World's Greatest Golf Jokes Compiled and edited by Stan McDougal; Paperback, with illustrations throughout. $4.50 (#62502)

Boxing Books

The Autobiography of Jack Johnson: In the Ring and Out; Paperback, illustrated w/photos throughout. $10.95 (#51358)

Boxing Babylon: Behind the Shadowy World of the Prize Ring by Nigel Collins; Hardcover, illustrated w/photos throughout. $18.95 (#51183)

Mike Tyson: Money, Myth & Betrayal by Monteith Illingworth; Hardcover w/8 pages of photos. $22.95 (#72079)

Muhammad Ali: A View From the Corner by Ferdie Pacheco; Hardcover, illustrated w/photos throughout. $21.95 (#72100)

A Pictorial History of Boxing: Revised and Updated Edition by Sam Andre & Nat Fleischer, updated by Peter Arnold; *Illustrated w/ nearly 2000 photos & prints.* Oversized paperback. $19.95 (#51427)

Baseball Books

Dodgers: The First 100 Years by Stanley Cohen; Paperback, illustrated w/photos throughout. $4.50 (#62508)

Five O'Clock Lightning: Ruth, Gehrig, DiMaggio and the Glory Years of the New York Yankees by Tommy Henrich w/Bill Gilbert; Hardcover w/8 pages of photos. $19.95 (#72101)

Great Moments in Baseball: From the World Series of 1903 to the Modern Records of Nolan Ryan by Tom Seaver w/Marty Appel; Hardcover w/photos throughout. $19.95 (#72095)

Say It Ain't So, Joe: The True Story of Shoeless Joe Jackson, revised edition by Donald Gropman; Paperback w/16 pages of photos. $10.95 (#51336)

(Prices subject to change; books subject to availability)